POKÉMON™

TRAINER'S JOURNAL

By Maria S. Barbo

SCHOLASTIC INC.

ISBN 978-1-338-60783-3

10 9 8 7 6 5 4 3 2 1   20 21 22 23 24

Book Design by Sarah Nichole Kaufman

Printed in China   68

First printing 2020

DRAW OR PASTE A PICTURE OF YOU AND YOUR POKÉMON HERE:

MY FAVORITE ...

Pokémon region: Hoenn

Types of Pokémon: Fidre ice Flyra

Pokémon Trainers:

Pokémon Gyms: Ash

Places I've been on my Pokémon journey: Hawaii

Pokémon I've seen but didn't catch:

Books: SHARK

Movies: miRACLe

Video games: SUPER MARI-OO

TV shows: DINO TRUCKS

Songs: ITSTHEFINALCOUNT
DOWN

Foods: WINGS

Things to do when I get home from school:
PLAYANDWATCHTV

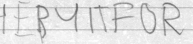

MVP! My Most Valuable Pokémon: piChy

My rarest Pokémon: ChYRMANDR

Legendary Pokémon I've caught: SC WRDL

Z-Crystals I've collected:

Badges I've earned: ГНЕВЧ ПРOR

PIKYCAY

A habit I'd like to make: EAV

A habit I'd like to break: NEVS

TOP FIVE

Top five ways you and your Pokémon love to have fun:
1.
2.
3.
4.
5.

Top five things you are really good at:
1.
2.
3.
4.
5.

Top five things you've learned from your Pokémon:
1.
2.
3.
4.
5.

Circle one you're going to teach a friend.

Top five things you can be even better at:
1.
2.
3.
4.
5.

Which one are you going to work on today?

TODAY I FEEL_____.

What makes me feel better when I'm having a bad day:

_____

What I do when I'm in a good mood:

_____

What makes my Pokémon feel better when they

are having a bad day:

_____

_____

_____

_____

_____

THINGS THAT MAKE ME FEEL . . .

angrier than a Mankey:	funnier than a Mr. Mime:
sleepier than a Snorlax:	grumpier than a Litten:
happier than a Blissey:	huggier than a Bewear:
more stressed than a Psyduck:	cooler than a Regice:
stronger than a Turtonator:	friendlier than a Rockruff:
more determined than a Pikachu:	slower than a Slowpoke:

IF I WERE A POKÉMON . . .

If you could be any Pokémon, which one would it be?

Why?

What strengths would you have?

What would be your best moves?

Draw yourself as a Pokémon here:

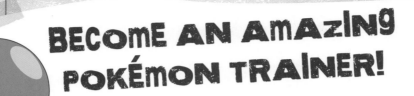

BECOME AN AMAZING POKÉMON TRAINER!

List the obstacles that stand in the way of you

becoming an amazing Pokémon Trainer:

Now what can you do to smash them?

who's on your team?

DRAW ALL THE POKÉMON IN YOUR POKÉ BALLS!

Pokémon name: Pichu

I caught this Pokémon when: 2022

Pokémon name:

I caught this Pokémon when:

Pokémon name:

I caught this Pokémon when:

Pokémon name:

I caught this Pokémon when:

Pokémon name:

I caught this Pokémon when:

Pokémon name:

I caught this Pokémon when:

MY BEST

Me vs. SNORLAX _____

Pokémon involved: _____

Moves used: _____

Coolest moments: _____

What I learned from the battle: _____

_____

_____

Me vs. _____

Pokémon involved: _____

Moves used: _____

Coolest moments: _____

What I learned from the battle: _____

_____

_____

Me vs. _____

Pokémon involved: _____

Moves used: _____

Coolest moments: _____

What I learned from the battle: _____

_____

_____

BATTLES EVER!

Me vs. _____
Pokémon involved: _____
Moves used: _____
Coolest moments: _____
What I learned from the battle: _____
_____
_____

Me vs. _____
Pokémon involved: _____
Moves used: _____
Coolest moments: _____
What I learned from the battle: _____
_____
_____

Me vs. _____
Pokémon involved: _____
Moves used: _____
Coolest moments: _____
What I learned from the battle: _____
_____
_____

ALL ABOUT MY FRIENDS

Draw or paste a picture of you and your friends with all your Pokémon here:

My closest friends:	PiCHY
Why we're friends:	BiKuS We PlAY
Their favorite Pokémon:	
Their favorite moves:	
If my friend was a Pokémon, they would be a:	
Because:	

Now fill in this chart
that's all about your friends!

NEEd a BOOST?

HERE ARE SOME POSITIVE THINGS ASH HAS
SAID TO PIKACHU ON THEIR JOURNEY:

"LET'S DO THIS!"

"YOU CAN DO IT, PIKACHU!"

"YOU'RE AWESOME!"

"GOOD JOB, PIKACHU!"

Write down all of the positive things your friends, family, teachers, and Pokémon say to you this week. Look back at them when you are feeling down, facing a challenge, or just want to smile!

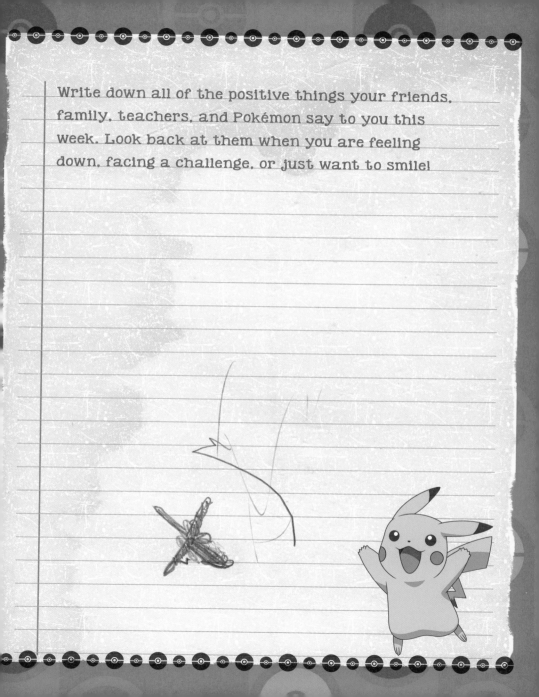

TOTALLY TERRIFIC

Make a list of your favorite Pokémon Trainers:

_____

_____

_____

_____

_____

What do you admire most about them?

_____

_____

_____

What can you do to develop those traits?

_____

_____

TRAINERS

What traits do you already have in common with them?

_____

_____

_____

Which Trainer are you actually most like, and how?

_____

_____

_____

_____

Charizard have an inner fire that drives them to keep trying their best even when things get hard—or scary. Write about a time you did something you were afraid to try. How did you feel afterward? FAIRD?

What would you tell a Pokémon who was afraid to try a new move? NRViS

What would you tell a friend who was anxious before a Pokémon battle? SCARD

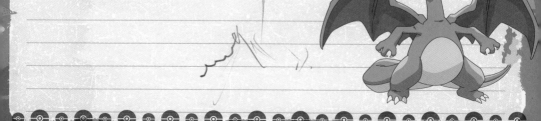

Team Rocket stole your Pikachu?

TEAMROCKET iWEPKL

You got invited to attend the Pokémon School in the Alola region?

A Bewear gave you a bear hug?

Your Popplio got upset that it couldn't blow bubbles?

Professor Oak asked you to come work in his lab?

You won a trip to the beach?

DESIGN YOUR OWN POKÉMON COSTUME

Which Pokémon would you like to dress up as?

What will you use to make your costume?

Which Pokémon will your friends dress up as?

Draw yourself in your costume here:

Name: _Pikachu_

Type: _Alfe_

Best moves: _____

_____

What will you say when
people ask about your costume?

" _____ "

THANKFUL THURSDAY

Every Thursday for the next four weeks,
write down four things that make you grateful
to have Pokémon in your life.

WEEK ONE:

1. _we give_
2. _____
3. _____
4. _____

WEEK TWO:

1. _____
2. _____
3. _____
4. _____

WEEK THREE:

1. _____
2. _____
3. _____
4. _____

WEEK FOUR:

1. _____
2. _____
3. _____
4. _____

Now look back at your list. What's the one thing that makes you the *most* grateful for your Pokémon?

WHO'S THAT POKÉMON?

Name: _____

Traits: _____

Name: _____

Traits: _____

Name: _____ SKYR

Traits: _____ FIRE

Name: _____

Traits: _____

Name: _____
Traits: _____
_____

Name: _____
Traits: _____
_____

Can you recognize these Pokémon from their shadows/silhouettes? Write down everything you know about them from memory. Circle your favorite traits!

Name: _____
Traits: _____
_____

Name: _____
Traits: _____
_____

POKÉMON PLAYLIST

What are the top ten songs
you like to listen to when training?

1.
2. POK
3.
4.
5.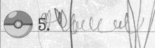
6.
7.
8.
9.
10.

TRAINER TECHNIQUE

What are ten ways your skills as a Pokémon Trainer have gotten better this year?

1.

2.

3.

4.

5.

6.

7.

8.

9.

10.

BEST TIME EVER!

What was your coolest encounter with a Pokémon ever?
What made it feel special? Write about it here.

TEAM WORK MAKES THE DREAM WORK!

Who do you want on your side when you're battling Team Rocket or competing for a badge?

MY POKÉMON DREAM TEAM:

1. Name: _____

Type: _____

Best moves: _____

Why I chose this Pokémon: _____

_____

_____

2. Name: _____

Type: _____

Best moves: _____

Why I chose this Pokémon: _____

_____

_____

3. Name: _____

Type: _____

Best moves: _____

Why I chose this Pokémon: _____

_____

_____

4. Name: _____

Type: _____

Best moves: _____

Why I chose this Pokémon: _____

_____

_____

What are the best qualities in a teammate?

Loyalty? Cooperation? Bravery? What do you think?

_____

_____

_____

WRITE FUNNY CAPTIONS FOR THESE PHOTOS OF POKÉMON.

WRITE YOUR OWN

Fill in the dialogue and captions to create a scene from your own Pokémon graphic novel!

Do you feel inspired to write a graphic novel about your own Pokémon? Go for it!

PRACTICE MAKES BETTER

Write about a time you struggled to do something.
What did you do to get better at it? How did it feel?

Now, think about a time a friend or Pokémon noticed something you worked really hard to do. What did they say or do? How did it make you feel?

Q8 WHAT'S BETTER THAN ONE PIKACHU?

A8 PIKA-TWO!

Pokémon love to have fun! Come up with your own
Pokémon jokes and puns here.

ALL ABOUT PIKACHU

JUMP-START YOUR DAY WITH THESE WORDS OF WISDOM FROM PIKACHU!

"Pika!"

"Pi-KA!"

"Pika, pika!"

"PI. KA. CHUUUUUUUU!"

List your favorite things about Pikachu:

1. _____

2. _____

3. _____

4. _____

5. _____

Pikachu's Top Five Best Battles:

1. _____

2. _____

3. _____

4. _____

5. _____

Draw a picture of Pikachu in action here:

THUNDERBOLT!

Write or draw all the things that scare you on this page. Then draw a picture of Pikachu blasting each fear with a THUNDERBOLT.

How will you conquer your fears today?

_____

_____

_____

_____

_____

_____

PHOTO BOOTH

Find pictures of your favorite Pokémon
and paste or draw them here.
List the top three things you admire
about the Pokémon in each image.

1. _____

2. _____

3. _____

1. _____

2. _____

3. _____

1. _____

2. _____

3. _____

1. _____

2. _____

3. _____

1. _____

2. _____

3. _____

1. _____

2. _____

3. _____

MAP YOUR DAY

Draw a map of your day here. Start with your home. Where did you go? Who did you see? What cool Pokémon did you meet or catch? Draw a star next to all the places you saw a Pokémon.

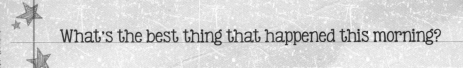

What's the best thing that happened this morning?

During lunch?

This afternoon?

After school?

Right before you started writing in this journal?

What was the hardest part of your day?

What made you feel better about it?

What is the one thing you can't wait to tell your

Pokémon about your day?

Draw the afternoon snack
you will share with your Pokémon here.

WRITE YOUR OWN

Use this story starter to write your own Pokémon adventure about Ash and Pikachu.

Ash and Pikachu were _____
(verb ending in "-ing")

through the _____ region
(region name)

when suddenly a _____
(Pokémon)

jumped out of the bushes.

Ash's reaction was _____.

But Pikachu's was _____.

And then, _____

_____

_____.

POKÉMON ADVENTURE

Until finally, _____

_____ .

" _____," Ash said to Pikachu.

"Pika!" said Pikachu. _____

The End.

Draw a picture to go along with your story here.

OBSERVATION STATION

Sit outside. Write down everything you observe for the next five minutes. What do you see—any Pokémon? Close your eyes. What do you hear? What do you smell? What do the smells remind you of?

dESCRIBE YOUR ROOM!

Where do you keep your training gear?

Where do you keep your notebook?

Are there any Pokémon hiding inside?

Where are the Pokémon hiding?

My favorite things about my room:

My favorite things to do in my room:

If I could change one thing about my room, it

would be:

POKÉMON SING-ALONG!

WRITE A SONG ABOUT YOUR POKÉMON!

Is it a pop song, a country song, or a hip-hop song?

What's the melody?

What are the lyrics?

Make up a dance to go along with the beat.
Draw the steps here.

Now perform the song and dance for your family,
friends, or Pokémon!

MAKE IT HAPPEN!

Use this space to make a collage using your favorite Pokémon photos or drawings. What does it say about what you want to achieve as a Pokémon Trainer? What makes you happiest about looking at this picture?

Have you ever had a dream about your Pokémon? Write and draw about it here.

PROBLEM SOLVED!

Challenge
1.
2.
3.
4.
5.

List five problems or challenges in your life right now.
How do you plan to tackle each of them?

Plan of Action	How my Pokémon can help

TACKLING TEAM ROCKET

Write the script for a conversation you'd like to have with Team Rocket. Convince them to stop trying to steal Pikachu! What would you say? What would they say back?

You: _____
_____

Jessie: _____
_____

James: _____
_____

Meowth: _____
_____

You: _____
_____

Meowth: _____
_____

James: _____
_____

Jessie: _____
_____

You: _____

Is there anyone in your life who is giving you a hard time right now? What are three things you can do to turn that relationship around?

1. _____

2. _____

3. _____

TOP TEN FUNNIEST TEAM ROCKET MOMENTS

LIST THEM HERE!

1. _____

2. _____

3. _____

4. _____

5. _____

6. _____

7. _____

8. _____

9. _____

10. _____

Is there something funny you'd LIKE to see happen to Team Rocket? Write or draw it here.

LAUGH OUT LOUD!

What are the funniest moments you've had with your Pokémon?

1.

2.

3.

What are some things you do to make your Pokémon laugh?

1.

2.

3.

What are some things your Pokémon have done to make you laugh?

1. _____

2. _____

3. _____

Which Pokémon do you think are the funniest?

1. _____

2. _____

3. _____

BONUS!

Can you write your own Pokémon tongue twister? Try it here!

_____

_____

WILD CARD

What are you thinking? What are you feeling?
What would you like to write about today?

EVOLVE!

When Pokémon evolve, they get bigger and stronger, and they gain new skills. What's a skill or strength you have that could be even stronger? What do you need to work on so that you could evolve into a stronger version of yourself? Plan your strategy here.

BE BRAVE!

What is the bravest thing you've ever done? How did it make you feel?

What is the bravest thing your Pokémon has ever done? How did it make you feel to watch your Pokémon be brave?

_____

_____

_____

_____

_____

_____

_____

_____

_____

_____

_____

_____

DECISION TIME!

Some decisions you make about your Pokémon are easy. Others are hard. Can you think of a time when you made a good decision? What helped you make that decision?

_____

_____

_____

_____

Can you think of a time when it was really hard to make a decision? What made it hard?

_____

_____

_____

_____

What are some things you learned from both
experiences about making good decisions?

What is the best feeling you've ever had? What made you feel that way? Tell your Pokémon all about it here.

LOVIN' LIFE!

THREE THINGS I LOVE ABOUT MYSELF:

1. _____

2. _____

3. _____

THREE THINGS I LOVE ABOUT MY FRIENDS:

1. _____

2. _____

3. _____

THREE THINGS I LOVE ABOUT MY FAMILY:

1. _____

2. _____

3. _____

THREE THINGS I LOVE ABOUT MY POKÉMON:

1. _____

2. _____

3. _____

THREE OTHER THINGS I LOVE:

1. _____

2. _____

3. _____

POKÉMON INVENTION

INVENTIONS HELP SOLVE PROBLEMS. AS A POKÉMON TRAINER, WHAT IS A PROBLEM YOU HAVE NOTICED THAT NEEDS SOLVING? WHAT KIND OF INVENTION MIGHT HELP SOLVE IT? PLAN YOUR INVENTION HERE!

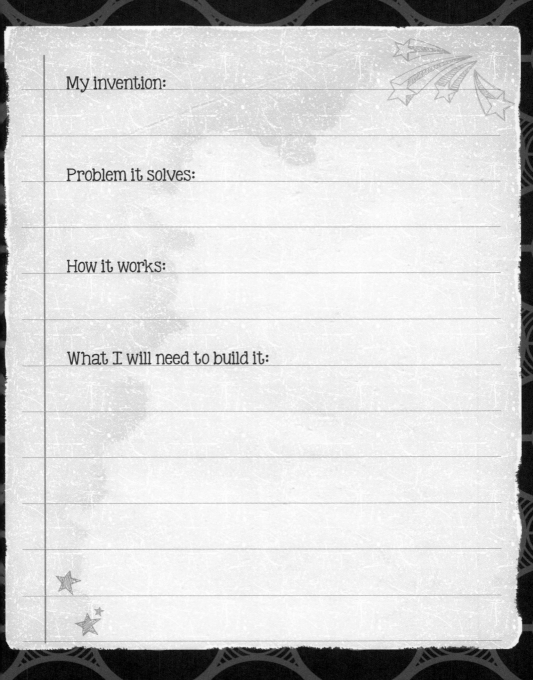

My invention:

Problem it solves:

How it works:

What I will need to build it:

WOULD YOU RATHER . . .

CATCH MEW OR MEET TAPU KOKO?_____
_____

Why? _____
_____
_____

BATTLE TEAM ROCKET OR TEAM SKULL?
_____

Why? _____
_____
_____

ENTER A POKÉMON PANCAKE RACE OR A POKÉMON PING-PONG TOURNAMENT?_____

_____

Why? _____

_____

_____

EARN A Z-RING OR WEAR THE WELA CROWN?_____

_____

Why? _____

_____

_____

EVOLVE YOUR CHARMANDER OR YOUR LITTEN?_____

_____

Why? _____

_____

_____

GO ON A FIELD TRIP TO THE ALOLA REGION OR PALLET TOWN? _____

_____

Why? _____

_____

_____

TAKE ON MIMIKYU OR MEOWTH? _____

_____

Why? _____

_____

_____

CATCH A RAICHU OR AN ALOLAN RAICHU? _____

_____

Why? _____

_____

_____

CATCH A WAVE ON A RIDE POKÉMON OR FLY ON A CHARIZARD? _____

Why? _____

_____

_____

GOTTA CATCH 'EM ALL!™

HOW WOULD YOU CAPTURE THESE POKÉMON?

WOBUFFET

I'd catch this Pokémon by _____

SHARPEDO

I'd catch this Pokémon by _____

BULBASAUR

I'd catch this Pokémon by _____

CYNDAQUIL

I'd catch this Pokémon by _____

PYUKUMUKU

I'd catch this Pokémon by _____

MIMIKYU

I'd catch this Pokémon by _____

MEMORY MAGIC!

Write down your best memories of hanging out with your friends, family, and Pokémon. What made each moment special?

Memory 1:

Memory 2:

Memory 3:

Memory 4:

Memory 5:

Now look back on your list. How does it make you feel to see so many happy memories in one place?

TIME FOR CLASS!

If you were going to teach a class at the Pokémon School, what kind of class would it be?

_____

What are the top three things you'd want your students to learn?

1. _____

2. _____

3. _____

What would happen on the first day?

_____

Books my students would have to read:

_____

Fun field trips we'd take:

_____

What would you give your students for homework?

_____

What would your students say to you at the end of the day?

" _____ ."

" _____ ?"

" _____ !"

Draw yourself as a Pokémon Professor here!

FLIP THAT FROWN

Think back to a really hard or sad experience. Now imagine that Pikachu had been standing by your side the whole time. Rewrite the story of that moment from Pikachu's perspective.

PLAN A SURPRISE PARTY

Is it a sleepover? A pizza party? Or an outdoor picnic? You decide!

Create the invitation here!

YOU'RE INVITED!

TO A _____ PARTY

TO CELEBRATE _____ !

WHERE: _____

WHEN: _____

BE THERE OR BE A SNORLAX!

FOR YOUR POKÉMON!

GUEST LIST

1. _____
2. _____
3. _____
4. _____
5. _____
6. _____
7. _____
8. _____
9. _____
10. _____

SNACKS

1. _____
2. _____
3. _____
4. _____
5. _____

GAMES

1. _____
2. _____
3. _____
4. _____
5. _____

PARTY PLAYLIST

1. _____
2. _____
3. _____
4. _____
5. _____
6. _____
7. _____
8. _____
9. _____
10. _____

WHAT'S IN THE GOODY BAG?

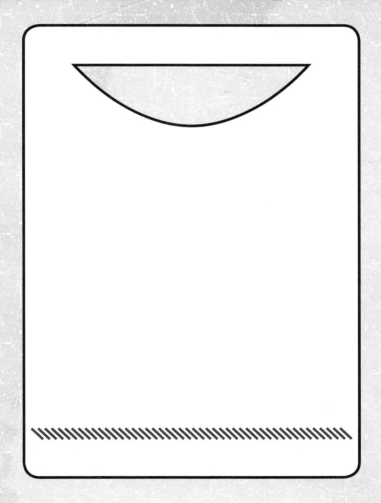

Now draw your ideas for party decorations!

STORY TIME!

Think about the most exciting adventure you've ever had with your Pokémon. Now imagine you were writing a book about it!

What would the book be called?

Which Pokémon would be the main character?

Which other Pokémon would be in the story?

Start writing the story here! Set the scene, and start describing what the characters are saying and doing.

_____

_____

_____

_____

_____

_____

_____

_____

_____

BATTLE OF THE BEST BUDS

FRIENDS HELP FRIENDS TRAIN THEIR POKÉMON. IMAGINE YOU AND A FRIEND ARE BATTLING HEAD-TO-HEAD. DESCRIBE HOW THE BATTLE PLAYS OUT.

My _____
(Pokémon)

VS.

_____'s _____.
(my friend's name)   (Pokémon)

Draw the battle:

My _____
(Pokémon)

VS.

_____'s _____.
(my friend's name)   (Pokémon)

Draw the battle:

NOW FOR A TWIST!

IMAGINE YOU ARE HAVING A POKÉMON BATTLE WITH YOUR BEST FRIEND . . . BUT YOU CAN ONLY USE POKÉMON WHOSE NAMES START WITH THE LETTER "B," AND YOUR FRIEND CAN ONLY USE POKÉMON WHOSE NAMES START WITH THE LETTER "M." PLAN YOUR STRATEGY HERE!

MY TEAM OF POKÉMON:

_____'S
TEAM OF POKÉMON:

1. _____
2. _____
3. _____
4. _____
5. _____

1. _____
2. _____
3. _____
4. _____
5. _____

Our matchups:

_____ vs. _____

_____ vs. _____

_____ vs. _____

_____ vs. _____

_____ vs. _____

Draw the best battle in the space below.

TTYL, PIKACHU!

If you could text Ash, what would you talk about?
What questions would you ask him about training
Pokémon? Write your dream chat with Ash here!

You:

Ash:

You:

Ash:

You:

Ash:

Now have a group chat with Ash, Mallow, and Kiawe.

Name of the group chat: _____

You: _____

Ash: _____

Mallow: _____

Ash: _____

Kiawe: _____

You: _____

Ash: _____

POKÉMON EMOJIS

Design emojis of your favorite Pokémon!

WILD CARD

Write about whatever you want!

ALL THE FEELS

Draw or describe how you feel ...

BEFORE A POKÉMON BATTLE:

WHEN YOU ARE ABOUT TO CATCH A RARE POKÉMON:

WHEN YOU ARE ABOUT TO TAKE A POKÉMON TEST:

WHEN YOU AND YOUR FRIENDS ARE
TALKING ABOUT YOUR POKÉMON:

WHEN YOU ARE ABOUT TO GO ON A
JOURNEY WITH YOUR POKÉMON:

WHEN YOU ARE HANGING OUT WITH
YOUR POKÉMON IN THE PARK:

HELPING HAND

Write about a time you helped a friend or Pokémon.
What did you do? How did it feel?

Now write about a time a friend or Pokémon helped you out when you were struggling. What did they do or say? How did it feel?

What are five things you can do this weekend to help your friends, family, and Pokémon?

1.

2.

3.

4.

5.

BE A BESTSELLER!

Congratulations! You just wrote a bestselling book about Pokémon. What is the title? Design the book's front cover here.

BY BESTSELLING AUTHOR

Don't forget the back cover!

Write a summary of the book here:

Praise for _____

(Insert title of your book here)

"AWESOME!" –Ash

"PHENOMENAL!" –Professor Kukui

"THIS IS SO COOL!" –Sophocles

"PIKA! PIKA!" –Pikachu

POKÉMON POWER

Close your eyes and imagine you just won an exciting and important Pokémon battle. How does it feel? What did you do to get here?

Describe or draw your happy place! How many
Pokémon are there with you?

DREAM BIG!

Write three goals you want to achieve in the next six months.

1. SCORGOIJASHAKI
2. _____
3. _____

What actions you will take to achieve them?

1. _____
2. _____
3. _____

Which Pokémon will be by your side cheering you on?

1. _____
2. _____
3. _____

Which friends will have your back?

1. _____
2. _____
3. _____

Now go for it!
Ash and Pikachu
believe in you!